YEAR 1 - Comprehension
Fiction, Non - Fiction and Poetry Texts in Themes

Introduction
Year 1 Comprehension is a collection of fiction, non-fiction and poetry texts grouped in themes suitable for the age group. These exercises can be used to introduce children to reading comprehension or used alongside themes the class may be studying at the time. The question pages are split into two sections. Section A has missing words or phrases to find, Section B requires the pupil to answer with a complete sentence. All the pages have been printed 'Landscape' to make maximum use of the space on Interactive Whiteboards. Black and white images are used in the paper book; full colour images have been used in the e.book and download.

Texts written by:
Peter Bell, Heather Bell and Kath Cope

Topical Resources publishes a range of Educational Materials for use in Primary Schools and Pre-School Nurseries and Playgroups.

For the latest catalogue
Tel 01772 863158
Fax 01772 866153
Email: sales@topical-resources.co.uk

Visit our Website at:
www.topical-resources.co.uk

Copyright © Peter Bell
First Published January 2013
ISBN 978-1-909458-00-0

Illustrated by John Hutchinson, Art Works, Fairhaven, 69 Worden Lane, Leyland, Preston
Designed by Paul Sealey, PS3 Creative, 3 Wentworth Drive, Thornton, Lancashire
Printed in the UK for 'Topical Resources Ltd' by T. Snape and Co Ltd., Boltons Court, Preston, Lancashire

Topical Resources is the trading name of Topical Resources Ltd, registered in England number 8072582.
Registered office: Jumps Farm, Durton Lane, Broughton, Preston, Lancashire. PR3 5LE

Contents

Curly the Doll

Curly is my best doll.

She comes with me all the time.

Mum took me to the carpet shop.

I left Curly in the shop.

I cried when I could not find Curly.

We went back and the man gave her to me.

Curly the Doll

Section A - Circle the correct answer.

1 What was the doll called?

    Carly   Crissy   Cathy   Curly

2 Which shop did they go to?

    paper shop   carpet shop   toy shop

3 Where was Curly left?

    in the car   in the street   in the shop

4 What did the girl do when she lost the doll?

    shouted   cried   went to sleep

Section B - Write a sentence.

5 Who gave the doll back to the little girl?

Doll's House

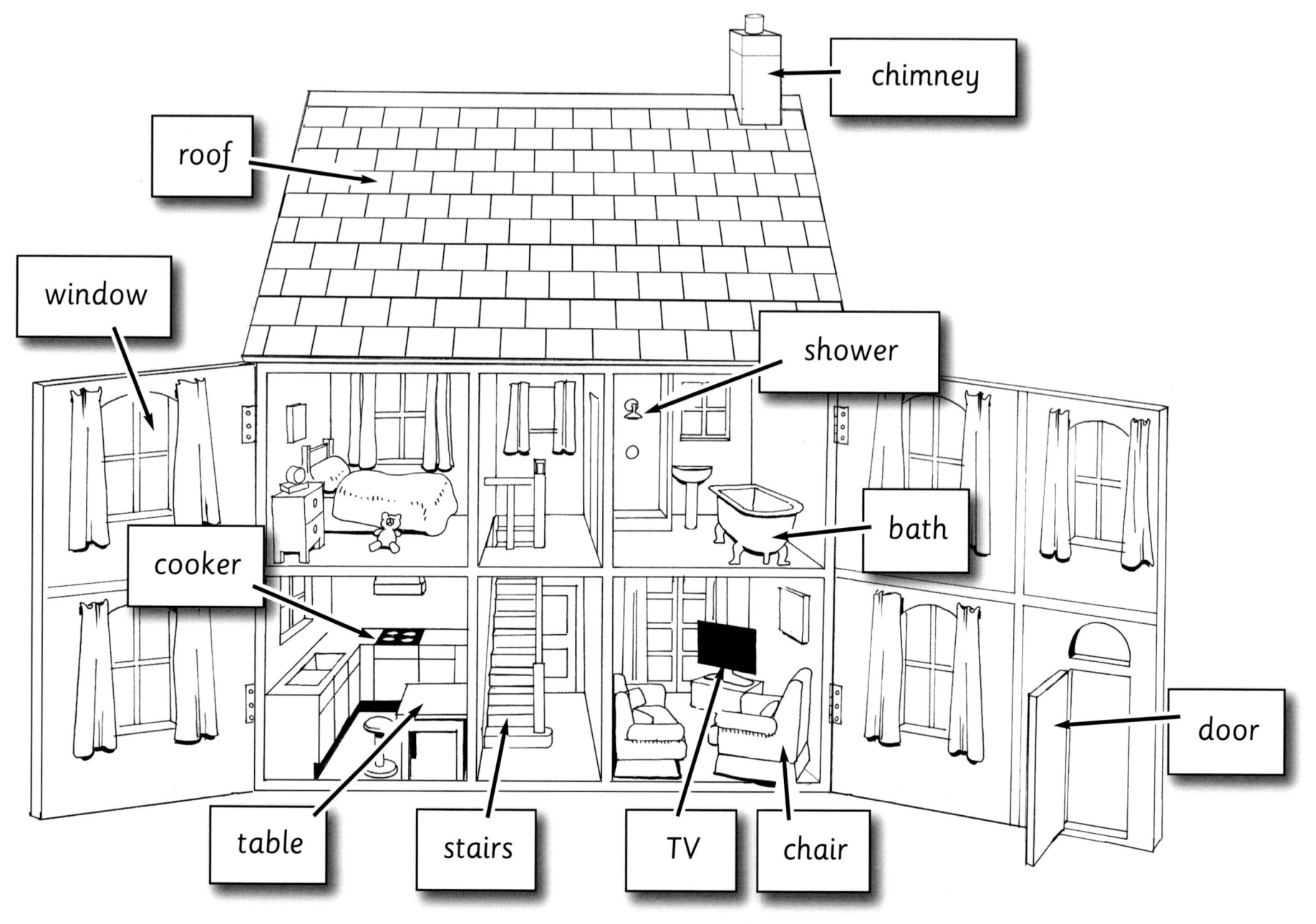

chimney

roof

window

shower

cooker

bath

table

stairs

TV

chair

door

Doll's House

Section A - Circle the correct answer.

1 How many chairs can you see?

one   two   three   four

2 Where is the table?

kitchen   bedroom   bathroom

3 How many doors can you see?

one   two   three   four

4 Where is the bath?

upstairs   downstairs   in the kitchen

Section B - Write a sentence.

5 Where is the chimney?

Toy Shop Window

Two little children,

Stop to stare,

A fairy doll, a toy car,

A furry teddy bear.

A train on a wooden track,

A plane up on high,

A doll's pram and tucked inside,

A dolly who can cry.

Toy Shop Window

Section A - *Circle the correct answer.*

1 How many children can you see?

  one   two   three   four

2 How much is the toy car?

  £2   £3   £4   £5

3 Where is the plane?

  on the floor   on a shelf   up on high

4 What is in the doll's pram?

  fairy   teddy bear   dolly who can cry

Section B - *Write a sentence.*

5 What are the children looking at?

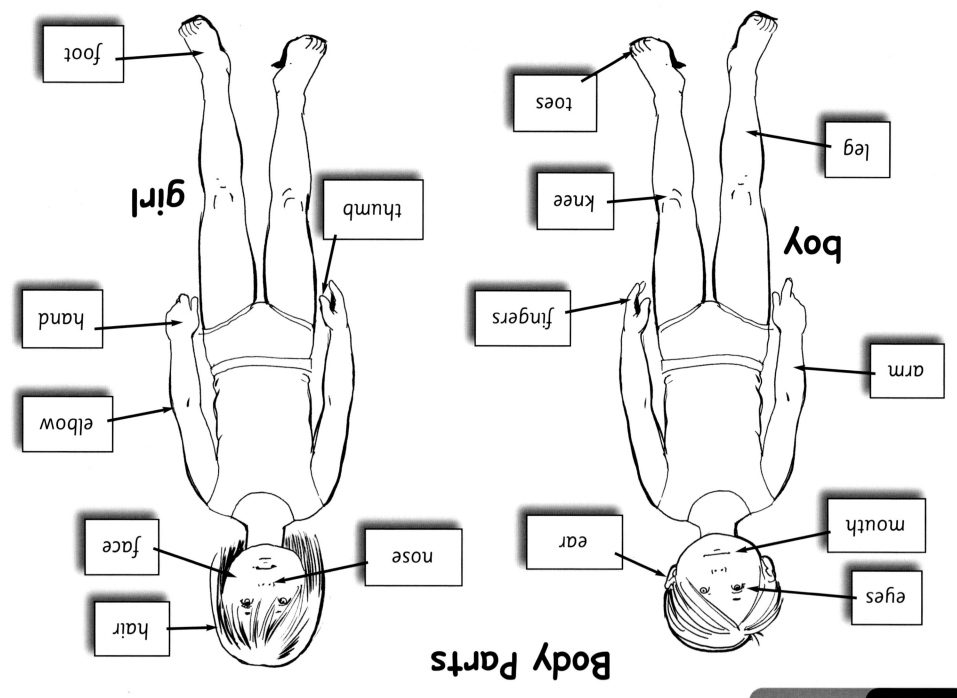

girl

foot

thumb

hand

elbow

face

nose

hair

boy

toes

leg

knee

fingers

arm

mouth

ear

eyes

Body Parts

Body Parts

Section A - Circle the correct answer.

1 How many eyes can you see?

one   two   three   four

2 How many thumbs can you see?

one   two   three   four

3 How many toes has the boy got?

4   5   8   10

4 Where is the knee?

on the arm   on the leg   on the head

Section B - Write a sentence.

5 Who has the longest hair?

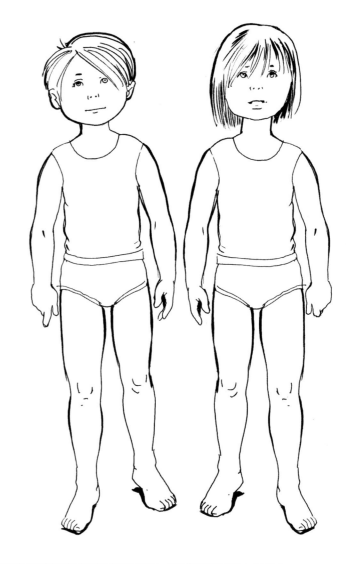

9

At The Park

On Saturday my family went to the park.

I went on the slide.

My sister went on the swing.

We both went on the see-saw.

Mum made us a picnic.

We fed the ducks.

We flew kites.

At the Park

Section A - Circle the correct answer.

1 Who went on the swing?

Mum   Dad   my sister   my brother

2 Who made a picnic?

Mum   Dad   my sister   my brother

3 What did the children feed?

hens   ducks   fish   the dog

4 What did the children fly?

a plane   a kite   a flag

Section B - Write a sentence.

5 Who went to the park?

Keeping Healthy

To keep your body healthy you must do these things.

Eat some fruit and vegetables.

Brush your teeth every day.

Keep your body nice and clean.

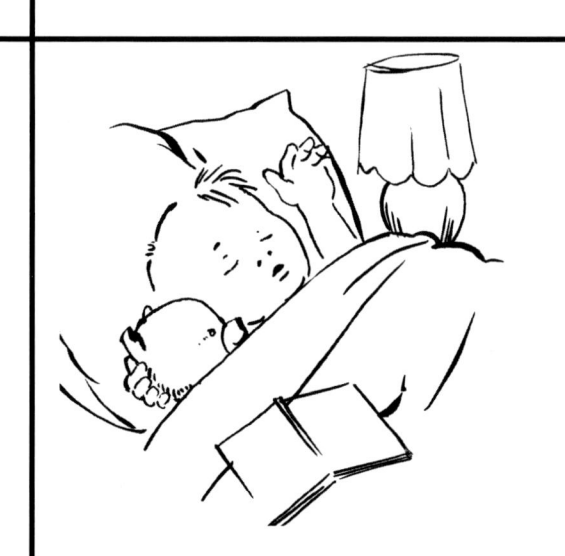

Rest and take exercise.

Keeping Healthy

Section A - Circle the correct answer.

1 To keep healthy you must eat...

fish and chips   fruit and vegetables

2 How often should you brush your teeth?

every hour   every day   every week   every month

3 What must you keep nice and clean?

your house   your bike   your body   your clothes

4 What can you do to rest your body?

go to the swings   go to bed   go swimming

Section B - Write a sentence.

5 What can you do to exercise your body?

First Day at School

I said goodbye to my mum at the school gate.

Our teacher Mrs King was waiting for us.

I sat next to a boy called Jack.

I drew a picture of my mum.

Jack and I played with the Lego.

Mrs King told us a story. She is very kind.

First Day at School

Section A - Circle the correct answer.

1 Who said goodbye at the school gate?

   Mum   Dad   Gran   Grandad

2 Who did the girl sit next to?

   John   Jim   Jazz   Jack

3 What did the girl draw a picture of?

   Dad   brother   Mum   sister

Section B - Write a sentence.

4 Who told a story?

5 What did Jack play with?

In the Classroom

abcdefghij klmno pqrstuvwxyz

outside play

slide

door

bike

white board

window

lunch boxes

car

computer

trays

paintings

coats

sand tray

teacher's desk

teacher's chair

paints

water play

tables

carpet

play house

chairs

In the Classroom

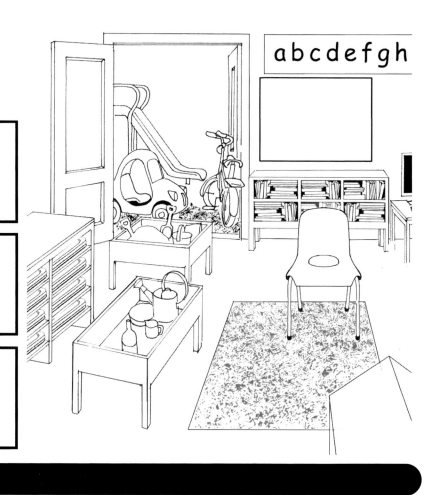

abcdefgh

Section A - Circle the correct answer.

1 What can you play with outside?

sand   water   paints   slide

2 Where are the paintings?

on the carpet   on the table   on the wall

3 Where is the teacher's desk?

under the window   on the carpet

Section B - Write a sentence.

4 Where is the teacher's chair?

5 How many paintings can you see?

Sports Day

We had a sports day at our school.

John won the egg and spoon race.

Jill won the sack race.

We had ice-creams at play time.

Tom won the long jump.

Ann and Raj won the 3 legged race.

The last race was for mums and dads.

18

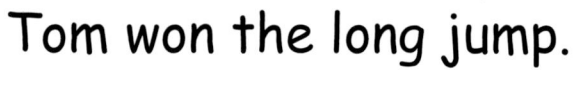

Sports Day

Section A - Circle the correct answer.

1 Who won the egg and spoon race?

Jill   John   Jack   Jade

2 Who won the sack race?

Jill   John   Jack   Jade

3 Which two children won the 3 legged race?

John and Jill   Ann and Raj   Tom and John

Section B - Write a sentence.

4 When did the children have ice-cream?

5 Who was the last race for?

Parts of a House

chimney pot

roof tiles

bricks

drain pipe

window

green house

garage

fence

door

door handle

grass

drive

flower bed

pond

path

Parts of a House

Section A - Circle the correct answer.

1 What is the roof made from?

tiles   bricks   curtains   grass

2 What are the walls made from?

tiles   bricks   curtains   grass

3 How many doors can you see?

one   two   three   four   five

Section B - Write a sentence.

4 How many flowers are in the garden?

5 Where is the chimney pot?

Moving House

Mum wanted a house with a garden.

Dad sold our house.

I was very sad.

We packed all our things into boxes.

A big van took the boxes to a new house.

The new house had a garden.

I was very happy.

Moving House

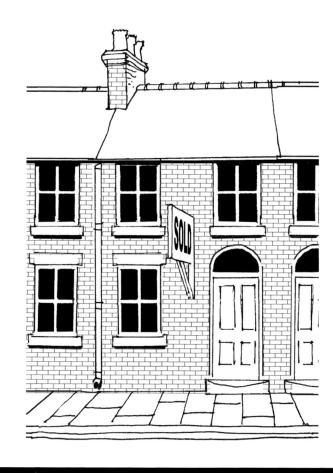

Section A - Circle the correct answer.

1 Why did Mum want to move house?

more space   a garden   new kitchen

2 Who sold the house?

Mum   Dad   Uncle   Nanna

3 What took the boxes to the new house?

a bus   a car   a lorry   a van

Section B - Write a sentence.

4 How did the boy feel when his house was sold?

5 How did the boy feel when he moved to his new house?

23

Different Homes

People live in many different types of home.

Some people live in homes
made of bricks.

Some people live in homes made
of mud and straw.

Some people live in caravans
and some live on house boats.

Some people live in
tents called teepees.

Different Homes

Section A - Circle the correct answer.

1 Some people live in homes made of...

blocks   bricks   sand   grass

2 Some people live in homes made of...

sticks and stones   mud and straw

3 A teepee is a ...

house   hotel   tent   caravan

Section B - Write a sentence.

4 What sort of home could you pull with a car?

5 What sort of homes float?

In the Garden Shed

bucket

soil

lawn mower

spade

table

logs

door

rake

plant pots

shelf

leaf

seeds

flower

hammer

saw

Theme 5 Plants Labels

In the Garden Shed

Section A - Circle the correct answer.

1 How many flowers are in the picture?

   one   two   three   four

2 Where are the seeds?

   on the floor   on a shelf   on the table

3 Where is the lawn mower?

   on the floor   on a shelf   on the table

Section B - Write a sentence.

4 What is in the bag on the floor?

5 Name the tools you can see.

How to Plant a Bulb

soil

plant pot

watering can

bulb

This is what you will need.

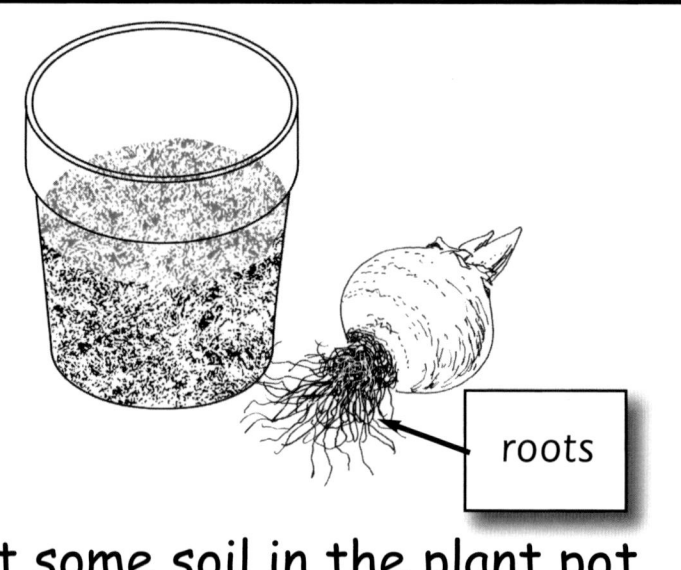

roots

Put some soil in the plant pot.

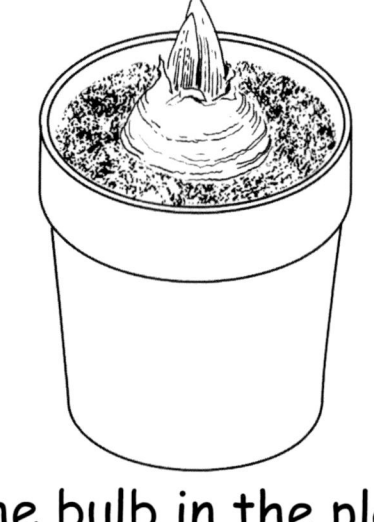

Stand the bulb in the plant pot and cover with soil.

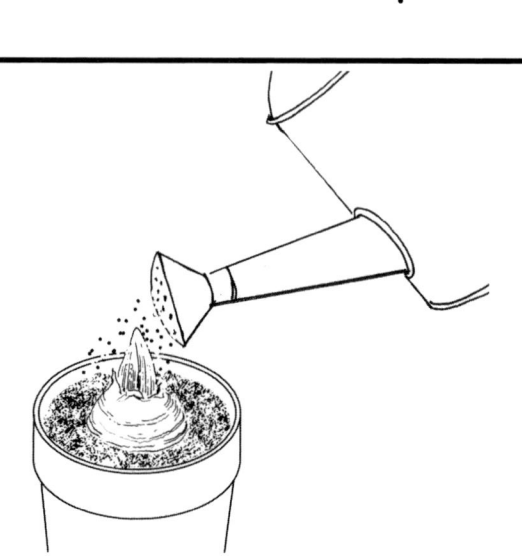

Water the bulb with a watering can.

How to Plant a Bulb

Section A - Circle the correct answer.

1 What goes in the plant pot first?

   soil   bulb   water

2 What goes in the plant pot next?

   soil   bulb   water

3 What do you cover the bulb with?

   soil   bulb   water

Section B - Write a sentence.

4 How do you water a bulb?

5 What do you need to plant a bulb?

Five Little Flowers

Five little flowers growing by the door,

Along came a gust of wind, then there were four.

Four little flowers for all the world to see,

My friend Tom picked one, then there were three.

Three little flowers glistening with the dew,

A naughty dog jumped on one, then there were two.

Two little flowers growing in the sun,

A fluffy bunny nibbled, then there was one.

One little flower standing all alone,

My Mum would like you, I think I'll take you home!

Five Little Flowers

Section A - Circle the correct answer.

1 What took away the first flower?

    rain   snow   wind   frost

2 Who took away the second flower?

    dog   Tom   bunny   Mum

3 Who took away the third flower?

    Mum   dog   Tom   bunny

Section B - Write a sentence.

4 What did the fluffy bunny do?

5 What would Mum like?

Baby Jesus

A star could be seen over a stable.

Mary and Joseph were staying there.

Baby Jesus was born. They put him in a crib.

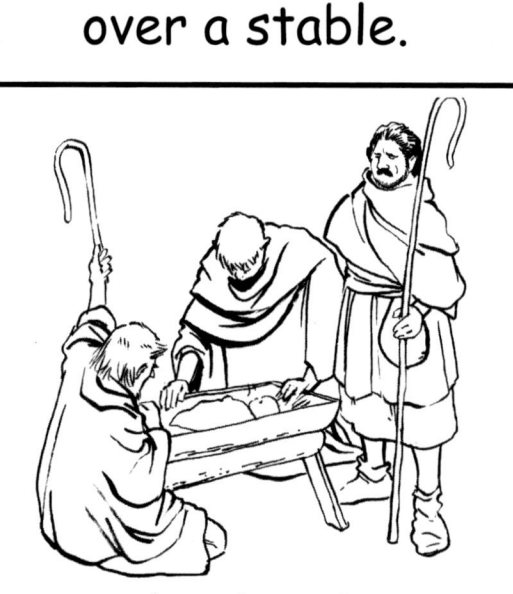

Some shepherds came to see the baby.

Some wise men came to see the baby.

The wise men brought some presents.

Baby Jesus

Section A - Circle the correct answer.

1 A star could be seen over a ...

stable   field   crib   barn

2 They put baby Jesus in a ...

box   cot   crib   present

Section B - Write a sentence.

3 Who came to see the baby first?

4 Who also came to see the baby?

5 What did the wise men bring for the baby?

How to Wrap a Present

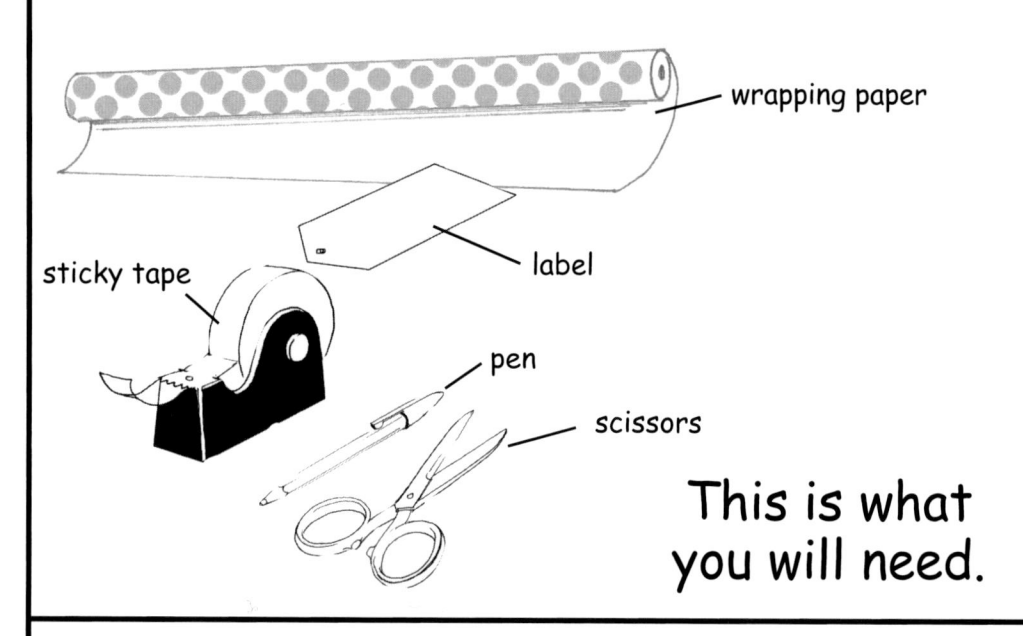

wrapping paper

label

sticky tape

pen

scissors

This is what you will need.

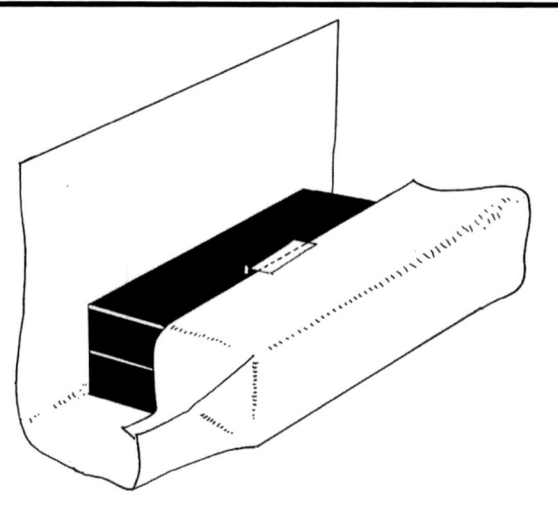

Wrap the paper round the present.

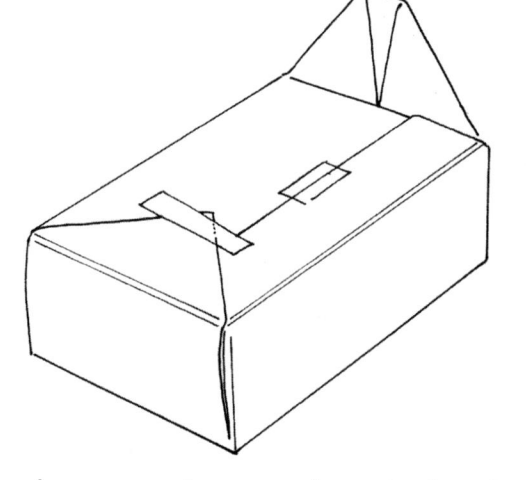

Fold the ends and stick down with sticky tape.

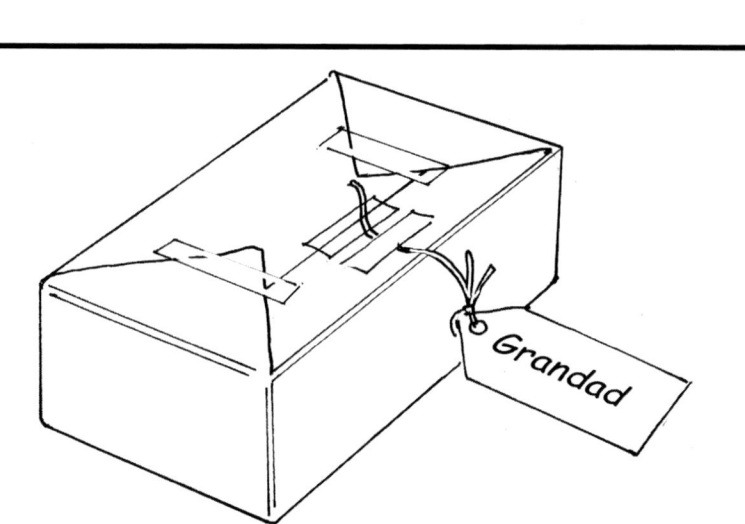

Grandad

Write a name on the label and stick to the present.

How to Wrap a Present

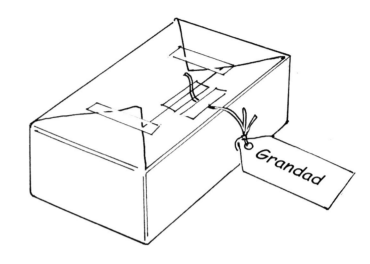

Section A - Circle the correct answer.

1 What is the first thing you wrap round a present?

sticky tape   paper   label

2 What do you do with the ends of the paper?

fold   bend   wrap   tear

Section B - Write a sentence.

3 What do you use to stick the end of the paper in place?

4 What do you write on the label?

5 How do you fasten the label to the present?

What's in the Box?

Shake it, shake it,
What could it be?
A red car, a wooden train,
Something just for me!

Prod it, poke it,
What could it be?
A new book, a puzzle too,
Something just for me!

Hold it, squeeze it,
What could it be?
A cuddly Ted, a Jack in the box,
Something just for me!

Shake it, prod it,
What could it be?
I wonder what is hidden inside?
You'll have to wait and see!

What's in the Box?

Section A - *Circle the correct answer.*

1 What colour is the car in this poem?

blue   green   yellow   red

2 What is the train made out of?

card   plastic   wood   metal

Section B - *Write a sentence.*

3 Why would you shake this box?

4 Why would you squeeze this box?

5 Who do you think could have sent this present?

The Three Little Pigs

The three pigs left their mummy's home.

The first pig built
a house of straw.

The second pig built
a house of sticks

The third pig built
a house of bricks.

The wolf blew down
the house of straw.

The wolf blew down
the house of sticks.

The wolf could not blow
down the house of bricks.

The Three Little Pigs

Section A - Circle the correct answer.

1 The first pig built a house of ...

stones   straw   sticks   bricks

2 The second pig built a house of ...

plastic   wood   metal   sticks

Section B - Write a sentence.

3 What did the third pig build a house from?

4 Which houses did the wolf blow down?

5 Why could the wolf not blow down the house of bricks?

How to Make a House of Sticks

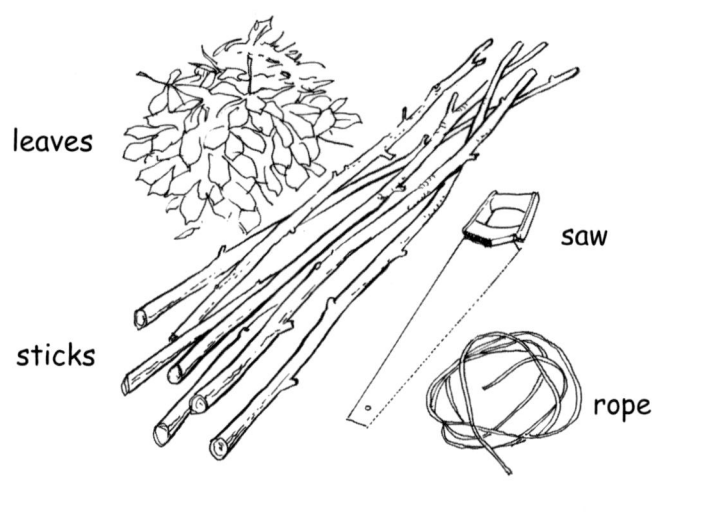

leaves

sticks

saw

rope

This is what you will need.

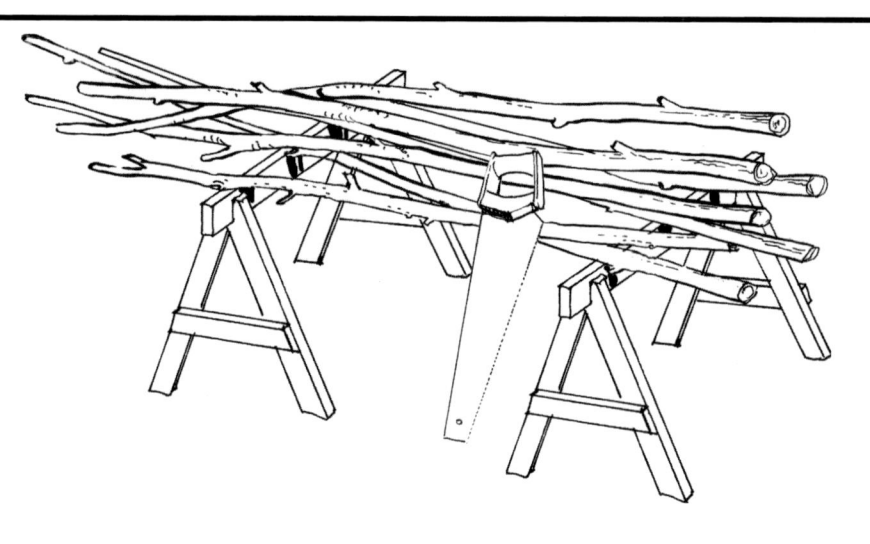

Cut the sticks to the same length.

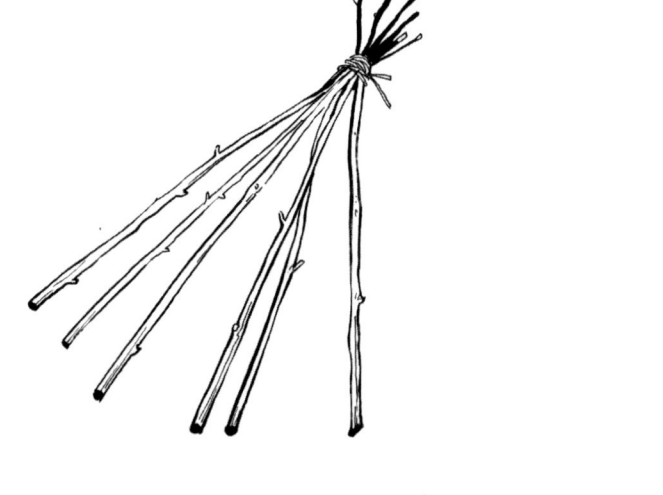

Tie the sticks together at one end.

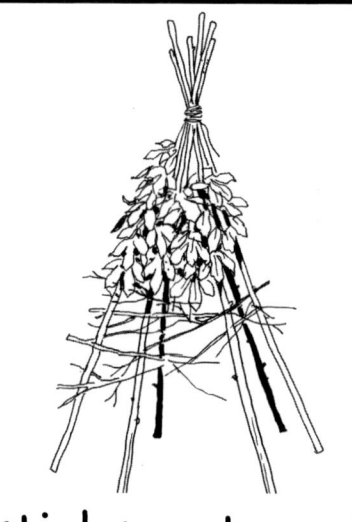

Stand the sticks up to make a tent shape.
Cover with small sticks and leaves.

How to Make a House of Sticks

Section A - Circle the correct answer.

1 What do you use to cut the sticks?

hammer   nail   saw   rope

2 What do you use to tie the sticks together?

hammer   nail   saw   rope

Section B - Write a sentence.

3 What shape is the stick house?

4 What is the stick house covered in?

5 What do you need to build a house of sticks?

All About the Pigs' Houses

The three pigs built very different houses.

The Straw House

- made of straw
- quick to build
- easy to blow down

The Stick House

- made of sticks
- took longer to build
- quite easy to blow down

The Brick House

- made of bricks
- took a long time to build
- could not be blown down

All About the Pigs' Houses

Section A - Circle the correct answer.

1 Which house was quick to build?

   straw house   stick house   brick house

2 Which house could not be blown down?

   straw house   stick house   brick house

Section B - Write a sentence.

3 Which house was easy to blow down?

4 Which house took a long time to build?

5 Which do you think was the strongest house?

Baby's Room

Baby's Room

1 Where does the baby sleep at night?

car seat   cot   pram

2 How many wheels are on the pram?

2   3   4   5

Section B - Write a sentence.

3 What is in the wardrobe?

4 What is used to clean the baby?

5 How many toys can you see?

Birthday

It was my second birthday.

The postman brought some cards.	 My mum made me a cake.	 My family came to visit.
 I opened my presents.	 I blew out the candles on the cake.	My family sang 'Happy Birthday' to me.

Birthday

Section A - Circle the correct answer.

1 Who brought the birthday cards?

Mum   Dad   family   postman

2 Who made the birthday cake?

Mum   Dad   family   postman

Section B - Write a sentence.

3 Who came to visit?

4 What happened to the candles?

5 Who sang 'Happy Birthday'?

Nursery School

When you are 3 you can go to nursery school.

At nursery school you can play in the sand.

At nursery school you can listen to stories.

At nursery school you can play outside.

At nursery school you can paint pictures.

Nursery School

Section A - Circle the correct answer.

1 At what age can you go to nursery school?

2   3   4   5

2 At nursery school you can play in the ...

woods   sand   soil   garden

Section B - Write a sentence.

3 What can you listen to at nursery school?

4 What can you play on outside at nursery school?

5 What can you paint at nursery school?

(NB: When answers are given as full sentences they are examples only)

Page 3 - Curly the Doll

Section A
1) Curly
2) Carpet shop
3) In the shop
4) Cried

Section B
5) The man in the carpet shop gave the doll back to the little girl.

Page 5 - Doll's House

Section A
1) Two
2) Kitchen
3) Three
4) Upstairs

Section B
5) The chimney is on the roof.

Page 7 - Toy Shop Window

Section A
1) Two
2) £3
3) Up on high
4) Dolly who can cry

Section B
5) The children are looking at the toys in the toy shop window.

Page 9 - Body Parts

Section A
1) Four
2) Four
3) 10
4) On the leg

Section B
1) The girl has the longest hair.

Page 11 - At the Park

Section A
1) My sister
2) Mum
3) Ducks
4) A kite

Section B
5) The family went to the park.

Page 13 - Keeping Healthy

Section A
1) Fruit and vegetables
2) Every day
3) Your body
4) Go to bed

Section B
5) Accept an answer that includes some form of exercise. E.g. You can go swimming to exercise your body.

Page 15 - First Day at School

Section A
1) Mum
2) Jack
3) Mum

Section B
4) Mrs King told a story.
5) Jack played with the Lego.

Page 17 - In the Classroom

Section A
1) Slide
2) On the wall
3) Under the window

Section B
4) The teachers chair is on the carpet.
5) I can see four paintings.

Page 19 - Sports Day

Section A	Section B
1) John	4) The children had ice-cream at play time.
2) Jill	5) The last race was for mums and dads.
3) Ann and Raj	

Page 21 - Parts of a House

Section A	Section B
1) Tiles	4) There are six flowers in the garden.
2) Bricks	5) The chimney pot is on the roof.
3) Three *(Front door, Garage door and Greenhouse door)*	

Page 23 - Moving House

Section A	Section B
1) A garden	4) The boy felt sad when his house was sold.
2) Dad	5) The boy felt happy when he moved to his new house.
3) A van	

Page 25 - Different Homes

Section A	Section B
1) Bricks	4) You can pull a caravan with a car.
2) Mud and straw	5) House boats float.
3) Tent	

Page 27 - In the Garden Shed

Section A	Section B
1) One	4) There is soil in the bag. on the floor.
2) On a shelf	5) I can see a saw, a hammer, a rake and a spade.
3) On the floor	

Page 29 - How to Plant a Bulb

Section A	Section B
1) Soil	4) Use a watering can to water a bulb.
2) Bulb	5) To plant a bulb you need soil, a plant pot, a watering can and a bulb.
3) Soil	

Page 31 - Five Little Flowers

Section A	Section B
1) Wind	4) The fluffy bunny nibbled the flower.
2) Tom	5) Mum would like the last flower.
3) Dog	

Page 33 - Baby Jesus

Section A	Section B
1) Stable	3) Some shepherds came to see the baby first.
2) Crib	4) Wise men also came to see the baby.
	5) They brought some presents.

Page 35 - How to Wrap a Present

Section A
1) Paper
2) Fold

Section B
3) Stick the ends in place with sticky tape.
4) Write a name on the label.
5) Stick the label to the present with the sticky tape.

Page 37 - What's in the Box?

Section A
1) Red
2) Wood

Section B
3) You might shake the box to see what sound it makes.
4) You might squeeze the box to see if you could feel what was in it.
5) Open ended.

Section 39 - The Three Little Pigs

Section A
1) Straw
2) Sticks

Section B
3) The third pig built his house of bricks.
4) The wolf blew down the house of straw and the house of bricks.
5) The wolf could not blow down the house of bricks because it was too strong.

Page 41 - How to Make a House of Sticks

Section A
1) Saw
2) Rope

Section B
3) The stick house is a tent shape.
4) It is covered with small sticks and leaves.
5) To build a house of sticks you need some sticks, leaves, a saw and some rope.

Page 43 - All About the Pigs' Houses

Section A
1) Straw house
2) Brick house

Section B
3) The straw house was easy to blow down.
4) The brick house took a long time to build.
5) The brick house was the strongest house.

Page 45 - Baby's Room

Section A
1) Cot
2) 4

Section B
3) There are clothes in the wardrobe.
4) Wipes are used to clean the baby.
5) I can see three toys.

Page 47 - Birthday

Section A
1) Postman
2) Mum

Section B
3) The family came to visit.
4) The little girl blew out the candles.
5) The family sang 'Happy Birthday'.

Page 49 - Nursery School

Section A
1) 3
2) Sand

Section B
3) You can listen to stories.
4) You can play on a slide outside.
5) You can paint pictures.